Published by Quotes Limited
Buckingham, England

Typeset in Plantin by
Key Composition, Northampton, England

Pictures Lithographed by
South Midlands Lithoplates Limited, Luton, England

Printed by Busiprint Limited
Buckingham, England

Bound by Cedric Chivers Limited
Bath, England

© Harold Bonnett 1988

ISBN 0 86023 344 8

Steam power has been my lifelong interest, and what happy hours I and many other Barkston schoolboys of 1915-1921 vintage spent gazing admiringly at steam engines! In summer, loud exhausting single cylinder plough engines tilled the village fields: Three and Four Cornered Spellers, Top Eight Acre, First Sands, First and Second Walks and so on. The old drivers, wearing oil-speckled round straw hats, let us stand on the bunker side plate where we had a grandstand view of everything that went on – sights, sounds and smells!

During the autumn and winter threshing season, out-of-school hours found us beside the gently puffing engine or humming drum in the stackyards of the village home farms. We also visited the tackles at outlying corn stacks beside hovels where cattle were straw-fed in winter: Walk's Hovels, Shelbourne's Barn or Beck Hovels.

For seventeen years I ran, as a hobby, two steam rollers Fowler no 17077 and Aveling & Porter no 12074. Having written five books about traction engines and two on railway steam locomotives, my researches for the non-traction engine parts of this one took me to the British Library, most of the Lincolnshire libraries and to Grimsby Public Library, and I have travelled about the county looking at old steam sites. I am grateful to a number of people for supplying photographs, and in particular to David Robinson for editing and preparing the book for publication.

When two visiting directors of American museums were over here in 1958, it was their expressed opinion that 'It was the men who drove steam engines that made the British Empire'. Lincolnshire steam men, known or unknown, dead or alive, share that glory.

## Key to picture credits

| | | | | | |
|---|---|---|---|---|---|
| A-B | Aveling-Barford | GS | George Storer | LLS | Lincolnshire Library Service |
| ABP | Associated British Ports | HB | Harold Bonnett | LS | Lewis Sommerfield Collection |
| AW | Albert Willis | HLS | Humberside Leisure Services | MS | Marshall, Sons & Co |
| BDS | B. D. Stoyel | HTDM | Hull Town Docks Museum | RAFCC | RAF College Cranwell |
| BSC | British Steel Corporation | HW | Henry Wilkinson | RSM | R. S. McNaughton |
| DAR | D. A. Rayner | JJF | J. J. Foreman | SM | Science Museum |
| DNR | David N. Robinson Collection | JR | Jack Rundle Collection | TR | Tom Redden |
| EWC | E. W. Carter | KM | Kodak Museum | YRM | York Railway Museum |
| | | LE | *Lincolnshire Echo* | | |

# Steam on the farm

A look over the face of Lincolnshire around 1840 would have shown the overall reliance of the county's farms upon the muscle power of horses, men and women. Water and windmills were numerous, but they played no part in tillage. The machine age revolutionised farming and steam was the power source.

Richard Hornsby, village blacksmith-cum-carpenter at Barrowby near Grantham made small manual threshers for local farms in 1814. The following year James Coultas of Union Street, Grantham made a horse-powered thresher. Contract threshing for farmers was undertaken in 1816, by the ancestors of the Marsh threshing family, Aunsby near Sleaford. Their thresher, maker unknown, and its portable horse-gears, were pulled around by four cart horses which, at the threshing, walked round and round in the gears to provide the power. By 1845 there were powered threshers with a daily output of ten quarters of grain. A quarter was a dry measure of eight bushels content that filled two sacks. Weight varied according to the crop — heavy wheat weighed 500lb to the quarter.

The first portable engine in Lincolnshire intended for agricultural uses was made in 1839 by William Howden & Son at their Grand Sluice Works in Boston, but the first practical one for steam threshing came from Clayton & Shuttleworth of Lincoln in 1845.

Within a dozen years they could claim that their threshing drums, knocking out fifty quarters of grain a day, had cut threshing costs by two-thirds.

Steam cultivation was accepted more slowly than steam threshing. The problem was that the heavy steam engines used most of the power pulling themselves over the clods, leaving little or nothing for a rear-hauled implement. This was overcome initially by using a stationary portable engine to drive roundabout style cable tackle, and from 1861 pairs of cable fitted traction engines, one on either side of the field, provided the answer. It was the manufacture of steam engines (except the cable style steam ploughs which were seldom a Lincolnshire line) and their associated threshing machinery that brought the Industrial Revolution to Lincolnshire towns.

About twenty Lincolnshire firms made both portable and traction engines. At Lincoln there were Clayton & Shuttleworth at the Stamp End Works (1842-1930); Ruston & Proctor, Sheaf Iron Works (1840-1918) continued as Ruston & Hornsby (1918-1963) and then as various subsidiaries; Robey & Co, Globe Works (1852-1985) and William Foster & Co, Wellington Foundry (1852-1960). In Boston were Wm Tuxford & Sons at the Boston & Skirbeck Iron Works (1842-1886); in Gainsborough, Marshall Sons and Co, Britannia Works (1848-1986); and at Grantham were Richard Hornsby & Sons, Spittalgate Iron Works (1815-1918), continued as Ruston & Hornsby (1918-1963). A late arrival at Grantham was Aveling & Barford, a 1931 amalgamation of the old Rochester and Peterborough engine makers; in 1934 they came into the Harrowby side of Hornsby's old works to make a limited number of steam rollers. The last Aveling-Barford roller left the works in 1950, when a final batch was contracted out to Armstrong-Whitworth's Openshaw factory in Manchester, so the final British steam roller was Lincolnshire designed but Manchester built.

The 1870s brisk trade for steam machinery, at home and abroad, saw a hectic expansion of engineering workshops. In

Boston, Tuxford's tall chimney half-rivalled the Stump as a landmark, and in Lincoln the wide scatter of works chimneys spread a grey smudge over the city. Around each big works sprang up long rows of red brick terraced houses for cheap renting to the thousands of new artisans — fitters, turners, millwrights, moulders, boilersmiths and carpenters. Hundreds of farm workers left the land for better employment in the town works, but continued living in their village homes. William Bonnett, the author's father, went to Hornsbys in the 1870s, walking the daily four miles to and from Grantham.

Peter Robert, 21st Baron Willoughby d'Eresby (1782-1865) of Grimsthorpe Castle near Bourne, pioneered the introduction of primitive steam engines to agricultural tasks in the period 1849-1854. He was also a close friend of Daniel Gooch, the celebrated locomotive engineer of the Great Western Railway. At least four engines were used at Grimsthorpe. The first was the 3½ tons 26 hp *California*, a twin cylinder, four-wheeled portable built in the GWR works at Swindon in 1849. There followed *Juba*, a Hornsby engine, and *Oasis* and *Australia*, both Swindon-made. All the engines were used for ploughing, sawing wood and stone, threshing, corn and clay grinding. In the period September to November 1854, *Oasis* threshed 40½ days and *Australia* for 16, using a threshing drum made by Hornsbys of Grantham, on work done for tenant farmers.

Lord Willoughby, living mostly at 142 Picadilly, frequently visited Grimsthorpe during the trials, but was often disappointed by breakages in the machinery. Indeed, the problems associated with a portable engine passing down the middle of a field with chain-drawn ploughs on either side of it, were never solved. A claim that this plough outfit,

operated by eight men and a horse to cart water, had displaced 16 ploughmen, and 32 horses, seems over-optimistic. Although the protracted trials at Grimsthorpe showed that one could plough that way, other people had perfected sounder steam systems.

At the Little Bytham GNR terminus of his Lordship's private steam tramway, in 1853 he converted the poky waiting room into the Steam Plough Inn, the only one of this name so far known. In the years following his death, one of his successors, with whom the amount of money spent on the steam ploughing experiments still rankled, had it re-named the Willoughby Arms.

Once started, Lincolnshire led the world in the development of steam-powered threshing machinery. Portable engines provided the power from 1842 to 1865, after which there appeared roving traction-engined tackles. Traction engines, however, did not immediately displace the old portables. Fosters claimed in the 1890s that they made ten portables to every traction engine; but the majority of foreign purchasers preferred portables for their cheaper price. As threshing was not a particularly hard job both portable and traction managed nicely within the 6-8 nhp (nominal horse power) range.

The make-up of a threshing set was an eight tons engine, five tons drum, and a one and a half tons straw elevator with, in some instances, a one ton chaff cutter. The daily hire charge in 1923 was £3, including the services of engine driver and the man who fed sheaves into the drum. Coal and water were the farmer's responsibility, along with the seven other men required.

In the early years good drivers were hard to get; some could neither read nor write, whilst others were unable to interpret the steam gauge figures, hence the red line still seen at maximum pressure point. At the 1872 Spalding Agricultural Show there was a best driver competition, using an 8 nhp portable engine as the test piece. Of the fifteen men who competed, several showed up badly. Board of Trade Inspectors, conducting 1880s boiler explosion enquiries, repeatedly drew attention to the fact that ill-informed drivers were a great source of danger. In 1882 an 1862 Clayton & Shuttleworth portable, owned and operated by Robert Woolridge at Crowle in the Isle of Axholme, blew up whilst driving a straw presser. His leg was broken and he was so badly injured that it was feared he would die. Four children playing near the engine fortunately escaped with slight scalds. The uninsured boiler had never been inspected by a competent person. Warning leaks had been ignored and in parts the eroded wrought-iron boiler plate was no thicker than an old shilling.

Drivers of threshing sets were paid a few extra shillings a week for their in-charge responsibilities. As the drum feeder had a harder and dirtier job than the driver, it was often the latter's custom to share in that work. Part of a driver's job was regulation of the drum mechanisms according to the crop. For mustard, the concave where the unthreshed crop entered the drum was opened out and all forced draught shut off; otherwise the tiny seeds were blown away. Any day-to-day complaints or comments made by farmers were directed at the engine driver.

Setting the tackle to a stack could be tricky, especially in wet winter weather when the engine often dug its hind wheels into soft stackyard ground. For positioning the engine the exact distance from the drum, some drivers carried a measured and marked length of string. Having fixed the distance, by squinting along the outer edge of the flywheel towards the outer edge of the drum driving pulley, proper alignment was determined before slinging on the sixty-foot leather or balata belt. Convex bevels on both pulley and flywheel ensured the belt held its driving grip.

In 1921 farm workers' weekly hours were reduced from 54 to 50 and for the first time there was a Saturday half day. At Barkston threshing began at 6.30 am, with a half-hour breakfast at 9, dinner 1-2 pm and a 5 pm finish, except on Saturdays when work finished at noon. A traction engine ran unhurriedly at 160 rpm, sufficient for its 4ft 6ins flywheel to spin the 7¼ ins diameter beater drum pulley at 1,000 rpm.

Catching rats and mice at threshing times was a seasonal sport with Barkston schoolboys. Farmer Joe Wadkin invariably built two big wheat stacks at Bottom Farm. They were thatched with the best wheat straw and left until the following February or March. Each stack took two days to thresh, and it was late afternoon of the second day, as the last sheaves were lifted, that the numerous rats and mice began to run out. Any boy who killed a rat made a name for himself. At the end of those early darkening winter evenings each boy took home, dangling at the end of a piece of binder twine, two or three of the fattest mice for his mother's cat.

Threshing was not unduly dangerous, but accidents did happen. Around 1900, Bill Wade, driving for fourteen-set contractors L. F. Morley & Sons of Skillington, was killed at the Bottom Farm there. Whilst oiling the engine slide bars and piston glands, the loose ends of the torn slop jacket he was wearing caught up on the spinning speed-governor balls, flinging him to a violent death. On 25 September 1903, Joseph Pell, working with Job Barman's thresher on Smith's farm at Little Hale, nearly cut through his big toe when the long handled hedge-cutting knife he was using for cutting straw bands of bean sheaves, glanced aside, and cut through his heavy boots.

Although steam engines threw chimney sparks or dropped red hot ashes from the ashpan in straw-littered stackyards, there were surprisingly few outbreaks of fire. In the late 1930s Fowler-engined tackle owned by Walter Marsh of Kelby near Sleaford was driven by Jack Elkington to the old stone pit site above the Little Hill at Barkston, prior to a threshing day for farmer Maurice Banks. The tackle was set to a barley stack, sheeted down and left around 4 pm. Within an hour a passer-by noticed a fire had started and raised the alarm. Jack ran from his lodgings in the village, found the engine still had plenty of steam, and backed it out undamaged. The fact that it was a waterless site, coupled with the late arrival of the Grantham fire brigade, meant that both drum and elevator were damaged beyond repair, and the greater part of the stack was burnt out.

Ernest A. Foley & Son of Meadowgate, Bourne, founded in 1890, were typical market town steam engineers and contractors, and a wide circle of farmers turned to them for light and heavy repairs to their own traction engines. They were also engine dealers, salesmen, and suppliers of engine oil and general requirements. Following the death of Mr Ernest in 1927, the firm's activities were cut down. At a three day sale in March 1928, ninety-one engines, representative of twenty makes, were auctioned, but the decline of steam power kept bids low. Twenty threshing drums, mostly by Lincolnshire makers, were also auctioned. Mr L. G. Foley, Ernest's son, carried on at the Hereward Works until 1930, when he sold out completely, parting company with the last four steam rollers.

In 1916, Redneck Watson, of Mill Farm, Barkston bought a USA International Harvester Titan motor tractor, which was used experimentally in 1919 for driving the family's old threshing drum, becoming the first Barkston farmer to thresh with an internal combustion engine. When the tractor was broken up, its broad-rimmed hind wheels became the village cricket pitch roller. What finished off steam threshing after 1946 was the winch-fitted, pneumatic-tyred tractor with ability to winch quickly when positioning drum and elevator (commonly called straw-jacks); also they ran unnattended for hours on end, using cheaper fuel. The end came in the 1960s when the combine harvester replaced both corn binder and threshing machine.

Steam tillage was a tough job requiring massive plough engines in the 12-20 nhp power range, or even higher. Steam work had two main limitations — the heavy engines could not get about in the wet fields in winter, and it was an impractical method of work in fields of less than five acres. However, the steam plough, using cheap coal and worked by determined crews, established itself as the first mechanised process for land cultivation. During the fifty years 1870-1920, big arable farmers relied heavily upon steam to do the hardest work, especially on heavy clay lands.

The early, clumsy roundabout cable tackles, with stationary engine driving a separate two-way windlass from which cables were led alongside the headlands, introduced ploughing by steam to British farmers. G. B. Skipworth of Moortown House, Caistor made his roundabout machinery mobile with an 1863 Richardson & Darley of Kirton in Lindsey 12 nhp traction engine. At Syston, Sir John Thorold used his 1872 Tuxford 12 nhp traction engine with a Fiskin style roundabout set-up. The last Lincolnshire roundabout tackle belonged to farmer Frank Cooke of Spalding, who worked it as late as the 1950s, taking power from a Foster traction engine. Very few of the windlasses belonging to these one-engine tackles have been preserved. John Fowler double-engined cable tackles, made from 1861, soon convinced farmers that steam cultivation was a worthwhile proposition. One tackle which cost £1,496 complete, operated by a four-partner firm of Wragby contractors, ploughed and cultivated 1,620 acres during 1884, a convincing achievement.

In 1882 there were eleven contractors in the county: Briggs Steam Cultivation Co, Collingwood & Lamb of Fulbeck, William Epton of Langton by Wragby, Joseph Cushworth of Alford, Samuel Dawson of Wyberton, George Shearman of Lincoln, Joseph Smith of Louth, William Smith of Sleaford, Chas Wright of Aswarby near Spilsby, F. & W. Ward of Boston and Quarrington, and Henry Yates & Co, of Grantham. It was farmer Fred Ward of Quarrington who, along with experienced steam-ploughman Billy Dale, founded the famous firm of Ward & Dale on Mareham Lane, Sleaford about 1890.

Lincolnshire villages welcomed the yearly visits of steam plough tackles. The melodic ringing of the engines' meshing gear teeth happily heralded their approach from miles away. Threshing drivers ambled along, but steam plough chaps, of a more vigorous breed, were always in a hurry, though pubs were never missed during opening times. Around Barkston in 1914-18, the April to November working season followed a farily regular pattern, and it was rare to see any but a Ward & Dale tackle in the 2,200 acres parish. The first job of the year was cultivation of the sandy fields. Farmers then harrowed out twitch to be burnt before the May sowing of swedes, turnips or mangolds. June was the time for cultivating clover and ryegrass stubble to make bastard fallow (not a full twelve month fallow). By pulling this land up into large clods and letting the hot summer sun kill the uprooted weeds, fields were put into a clean and healthy condition for autumn sowing of winter wheat, oats and beans. Throughout the summer the tackles never ceased work from first light until half dark. The cookboy in his van had meals ready for each man as he came in; meal relief for the two drivers was covered by the foreman, and the cookboy relieved the implement steersman.

Autumn was the time of greatest activity with the rush to break up the stubble before winter set in. One set of 12 nhp single cylinder Fowler engines coped with the work available within a two to three miles radius of Barkston. It would come from Silk Willoughby or Honington, to do a week's work in the parish before moving over to Foston or Marston. It came back for a fortnight to cultivate the clover stubble, and then off to Hough on the Hill.

The boiler of Fowler single cylinder engine no 1166 blew up November 1879 at Aswarby near Sleaford, and Fowler no 2909, or similar type, rent its boiler in August 1912 at Benniworth. Two men were killed in the first explosion and one in the second. In the case of no 1166, a steam and water leak was noticed the previous day, and Yates & Agnew, the Grantham owners, were advised. They sent foreman mechanic Henry Watkinson, with instructions not to caulk any flat plate. If in any doubt, the fire was to be dropped and the boiler plate drilled and tested for thickness, and he had with him a hand drill for the purpose. Watkinson arrived in Edward Baker's field about 2 pm, finding driver Sandy Cooper at work with a full head of steam, probably around

120 psi. There was a slight leak at the left side of the firebox outer shell plate, near where the driver stood. Ignoring his directive, Watkinson attempted to caulk the fracture. The boiler exploded along a nine and a half inches fracture. Watkinson was blown backwards fifteen yards; he died within two hours. His caulking tool was afterwards found in a corn stack 140 yards away. Cooper was flung upwards through an oak tree with great violence, breaking off a largish branch in his flight, before landing twenty-five yards away; a week later he died in Grantham Hospital. The engine went back to Fowlers, and was given a new boiler and general overhaul before passing into the ownership of Ward & Dale.

Steam cultivation reached its peak during the Great War when the need for food production was pressing. In addition to the old single cylinder engines, new compounds with economical two-stage steam expansion, and weighing 19 tons apiece, were offered more work than they could cope with. A John Fowler 1919 survey revealed a total of 586 tackles in England, Wales and Scotland. Lincolnshire, top of the county lists, had 107 sets operated by 55 different owners, with the greatest concentration around Spalding, where 11 of the 35 Fenland operators were based. Ward & Dale of Sleaford, with 25 tackles, were the largest operators in the country.

From 1918 onwards the decline of steam cultivation was rapid. American-made oil-engined tractors, imported in quantity during the Great War, had proved suitable for all but the hardest clay land work. By the mid-1920s compound tackles, which had cost over £4,000 in 1918, were seen laid up at times for want of work. As early as 1934 there were 45,000 motor tractors at work in Britain. Ward & Dale, after scrapping six sets of old single cylinder engines in 1938, carried on for another year with ten sets of compounds, charging the near cost price of 10s an acre cultivating. In March 1939 they sold out altogether. The lowest price for a pair of engines was £58 and the best a mere £140; implements also went at bargain prices.

# Steam on the road

Most British steam rollers were made by Aveling & Porter, the specialist builders of Rochester in Kent. Lincolnshire, however, had five makers: Aveling-Barford of Grantham, Marshalls of Gainsborough, and Ruston & Proctor, Clayton & Shuttleworth and Robey & Co of Lincoln. The era of these steam machines was from 1870 to 1970. They were owned by County, Borough or District Councils, or by private road rolling contractors.

When the Barkston by-pass was made in 1922, as an unemployment relief scheme, Kesteven County Council hired from a Sleaford contractor (probably J. D. Kent) a single cylinder, 8 tons, cab-less, spoked flywheel and green-painted Aveling & Porter steam roller. The driver's van and a two wheeled water cart were parked in farmer John Rilett's paddock at Pear Tree Farm alongside the village green. The driver lived in his van, except at weekends, when he went home by Lincolnshire 'bus, but once a month stayed the Saturday night in order to carry out, on Sunday morning, the boiler washout.

The author, then a 15s a week farmboy with John Rilett, was hired out, along with farm horse, Smart, to the County Council for the duration of the scheme. George Pullen, a shortish middle-aged man who lived at Carlton Scroop two miles away, was promoted from local chargeman road sweeper to site ganger. George, who had formerly been seen 'cycling through the village with a brush and shovel strapped lengthwise on his bike, now rose to be a small-time boss. Mr W. B. Purser, the Council's Sleaford-based surveyor, motorcycled over twice a week to cast a professional eye over the works; otherwise George was on his own. His weekly wage was unlikely to have been more than £3.

The only piece of machinery on that job was the steam roller. Horses carted the dug spoil, brought roadstone from Honington GNR station a mile away, as well as bringing down ironstone from the Little Hill stone pit. The men, mostly Grantham unemployed, were paid a daily flat wage, except when winning stone at the quarry, for which they were paid a piecework bonus on every cubic yard hacked out and stacked ready for carting away. This ochre-coloured stone, broken into slabs the size of a large dinner plate and four to six inches thick, eventually formed the upright foundation, or pitching, of the new road.

Roller drivers occasionally got on the wrong side of the police. Archibald McColl of Belton fell foul of Sergeant Cook in September 1937 for making excessive smoke as his roller passed through Wilsford. The Sleaford magistrate accepted the danger to other traffic and imposed a fine of 10s. In 1946, Baines & Co, long-established rolling contractors of Potton in Bedfordshire, came to Belton alongside the A 607 into buildings erected for WW2 manufacturing. Two years later their subsidiary, the Eddison Steam Rolling Co, of Dorchester in Wiltshire, also moved to Belton, and the undertaking was renamed The Eddison Plant Co. In 1955, when diesel rollers were fast displacing steam, about twenty redundant steam rollers, all Aveling & Porter machines, stood against the Belton-Syston parish boundary. None were for sale, except to Charles Spick, the Grantham scrapman. To prevent any would-be preservationist buying a roller and then undertaking contract rolling to the harm of Eddison's trade, holes had been burnt in the front tube plates as a precaution against future use. At that time one Belton steam roller only was at work, doing a road job at Foston in the hands of an old steam driver who did not wish to change over to diesel. When Eddisons moved to new quarters on Harlaxton Road, Grantham in 1965, they gave A & P roller no 10393 of 1922 to the Borough Council for permanent exhibition in a town park. (Note: The publisher's late father was Chairman of Eddison Plant Hire Co , and the publisher retains the brass horse trademark from one of the last road-rollers).

Four Lincoln firms made steam wagons; Clayton & Shuttleworth, Ruston & Proctor, Robeys and Fosters. Whilst the output of Rustons and Fosters was small, the other two firms made wagons in quantity. Over-type wagons had engines over horizontal locomotive type boilers, whilst under-types, with their upright boilers, had under-frame mounted engines. Following the easing of road speed restrictions in 1903, steam wagons ran at 12 mph, speeding up road transport and generating more interest in building these vehicles. Early wagons, like traction engines, had steel-shod road wheels, plain tyred in front and straked behind; but wagons always ran quieter. Wagon crews could sit down, whereas traction engine men usually stood up at their work.

Country town brewers found wagons ideal for beer barrel deliveries to village pubs. Mowbrays of Grantham ran a

Foden of Sandbach overtype beer wagon before the Great War. In 1915, Clayton & Shuttleworth landed a government contract for several hundred overtype wagons for the armies at home and abroad. Hundreds of surplus Clayton army wagons were assembled in 1919 at UK disposal points for auction. At a Reading 1920 sale, the auctioneer, stuck on a first bid of £300, told buyers to pick their choice, at £300 a wagon. Buckinghamshire timber haulier Francis Grover happily bought wagon no 47196, a five-tonner on wooden wheels shod with solid rubber. It was a great disappointment when he found the boiler tubes constantly leaked and none of the beading or expanding he did had the slightest effect. A year later a man took a fancy to the look of the wagon and bought it, cheaply. Within a week he asked for his money back.

Aiming at a better wagon, in 1925 Claytons turned out an undertype, having a pot boiler incorporating a stayless corrugated firebox, with water tubes strung across the combustion space above the fire. Unusually, these wagons had twin cylinder, single steam expansion engines. By 1929, the books of Clayton Wagons Abbey Works showed a loss of £550,000, and it was this, coupled with poor sales of wagons and Russian trade debts of £300,000 that brought about the closure of Clayton & Shuttleworth in 1930.

Robeys made smart looking over and under type wagons. Their late 1928 pneumatic-tyred overtype had a compound engine which ran on 200 psi steam, supplied from a locomotive style boiler embodying a round stayless firebox of great strength. A further refinement was totally enclosed motionwork and the crankshaft ran smoothly in ball bearings. Here again, lack of orders forced Robeys to abandon steam wagon building.

Strangely, none of the Lincoln steam engine makers progressed to manufacturing either agricultural motor tractors or road motor lorries. Fosters had co-operated with the Daimler Car Co of Coventry in the 1912-1914 so-called 'Plough Engine Project', in which an upstaged car-style Daimler petrol engine of 105 horse power in a Foster chassis formed an agricultural tractor; it was from this that the first British army tanks were developed in 1915. Clayton & Shuttleworth dabbled half-heartedly in pre- and post-war chain rail motor tractors, but nothing worthwhile came of it. On the other hand Marshalls of Gainsborough continued to turn out farm tractors until the firm was liquidated in 1986.

The heaviest and most important road haulage was undertaken by ten to 19 tons engines in the 8 to 10 nhp power range, known as road locomotives. Best known of these were the ornate and splendidly polished showmen's engines that reigned supreme in the public eye. On fairgrounds these magnificent steam machines generated electricity which lit and turned the 'rides'. On the road they hauled three heavy trucks of entertainment machinery, usually a 30 tons load, between one fair and another. The huge Lincoln fairs, held on the cattle market, presented the memorable sight of perhaps sixteen of these gleaming and majestic engines busy at work. Of the fun-making 'rides' there were flying pigs, moonrockets, helter-skelters, steam yachts, chair o'planes, Noah's Arks, Jack and Jill, roundabouts and electric railways.

William Burrell of Thetford and John Fowler of Leeds were the main builders of showmen's engines, with William Foster of Lincoln third with sixty-eight engines. Richard Hornsby made only one of these engines, the 6 nhp compound no 6292 of 1887, sold to Henry Thurston of

Stansted in Essex. The first Foster showmen's engine was the 1904 compound no 2981 *Reliance* sold to N. & J. Baker of Carlisle. It acquitted itself well over the hilly Border country; on one occasion Joe Baker drove the 150 miles from Newcastle to Kelvin Hall Carnival in Glasgow, stopping only for water, to buy coal, oil up, clean clinker from the fire, and eat a snack of food. In appearance, Foster's engines were good lookers, with mushroom-style chimney tops, that made them far more pleasing to the eye than the more powerful Fowlers.

The short intervals between fairs called for a fast, free-steaming, powerful and rugged engine able to scamper over the flats and climb the hills with ease. Mindful of these needs, Fosters fitted their fair engines with three gears: slow, intermediate and fast. The 300 gallons water supply permitted ten to twelve mile runs between water stops. On the last vehicle of those road trains rode the look-out man, legs dangling from the tailboard. When a long cord stretched along the van sides was pulled, it sounded a hammer-type bell in the cab of the engine. One ring meant stop, two was proceed and three called attention to a long queue of traffic behind. Reverse signals were sounded on the engine's whistle; one blast called for application of the hand brakes and two for their release.

Seven Lincolnshire amusement showmen ran fairground engines. G. Wilkie of Cleethorpes had Burrell no 3447 *Stirling Castle* of 1913, at Skegness Joseph Wingate had 1906 Fowler no 10690 *Willing*, and Boston-based Aspland and Howden toured 1906 Fowler 10696 *George The First*, and also 1912 Burrell no 3404 *Kathleen Mary*. In Lincoln were two Burrells owned by Charles Warren; no 1810 *Clarence* of 1895 and no 1985 *Mona* of 1897. Charles's son Fred bought Burrell

no 3932 new in 1922, naming her *Mona 11*. Eventually the Warren business became Smith & Warren, touring with two sets of roundabouts, a two and a three-abreast respectively, from their Snail Street depôt. Another Lincoln contractor named Storey sold his three-abreast roundabouts in 1921 to Fred Thompson of Skegness, who then bought new from Fosters, the *Wellington* type steam tractor no 14511 *Bonny Kate*. Joe Bland, a Grantham taxi proprietor, bought a rather run-down roundabout from a showman visiting the Mid-Lent Grantham Fair in the 1930s. The time-expired centre engine could not spin the machine unless a man was detailed to give a 'push-off' before each start. The Great War put an end to many village feasts, including that at Barkston held each May in association with the annual celebrations of the Blue Club Sick Society. But what finally put paid to showmen using steam engines at town fairs was the ready and cheap availability of surplus army heavy-duty motor lorries after the Second World War.

Road haulage with light loads was undertaken by 5 nhp steam tractors or 7 nhp general purpose engines, and 8-10 nhp unadorned road locomotives for the heavier jobs. About 1920 a large Fowler road locomotive sometimes passed Barkston school playground, hauling two heavily-built trucks laden with huge sawn blocks of the famous Ancaster building stone. Owned by Lindley Quarries of Wilsford Heath, this engine, driven by Henry Morris of Ancaster, was normally occupied taking stone to Ancaster GNR station with its special stone siding. The most notable traction engine driver in the Ancaster area about that time was Joe Beckett (1892-1956), the burly British and Empire heavyweight boxer. He appeared in Lincolnshire early in 1916 on road haulage work, taking building materials from

Sleaford and Ancaster stations for the construction of Cranwell Royal Naval Air Service plane and airship station. Once, Chief Petty Officer W. H. Whitlock, chauffeur to the Station Commander, met a 'monster' traction engine with a heavy load of steel girders, intended for the new hangers and completely blocking the rough farm road. Whitlock rather impolitely told the driver, with his coal-black face, to make way, not realising that the man threatening to get down and knock his head off was Joe Beckett.

Some big and powerful road locomotives, intended for the direct haulage of agricultural implements, were made by Fosters, Robeys and Marshalls. Although this trade was never great, batches of these Lincolnshire-made engines were sold abroad, where drier climates favoured direct traction cultivation.

# Steam in industry

The first steam power used in a Lincolnshire factory was probably the 8 hp low pressure beam engine, maker unknown, installed around 1800 in Mr Gouger's 'Silkschool' works in Stamford. Some four hundred poor women and girls worked at home doubling and twisting silk for further processing in the works. Another early engine, in 1835, pumped Trent water for town use at Gainsborough. Great Grimsby Royal Dock of 1852 was built with two steam engines. One, a Cornish beam engine made by Mr Mitchell of Perran foundry, Cornwall, pumped well water which maintained the level of the Royal Dock, until the supply dried up. The other was a Sir Wm Armstrong duplicate engine in which each horizontal section was rated at 25 hp, used to force water up into the 33,000 gallons water tank on top of the 309ft Dock Tower. This supplied the hydraulic power for operating the dock gate machinery and sluice doors, also the fifteen hydraulic cranes on the quays and in the warehouses. The engine was removed in the mid-1920s with the electrification scheme.

When Boston Dock was constructed in 1885, hydraulic power was provided from a pair of twin 15 inch diameter cylindered steam ·engines. At the 1855 Paris Exhibition, a Wm Tuxford & Sons portable engine drove some of the machinery.

There was a factory accident in April 1881, when Arthur Eyeions, aged 32, was killed when caught between two large cog-wheels on a large steam engine he was oiling at Simmons & Sons oil and cake manufactory in Boston. Steam engines could also be found in a village carpenter's shop. Edward Parr, the Barkston wheelwright and carpenter, used a small single cylinder horizontal engine, with a free-standing upright boiler, for driving a small circular saw, up to the early 1900s.

Grantham Urban Electricity Supply Co's East Street generating station (1902-1932) had four Bellis & Morcom, Birmingham, high speed vertical steam engines. A 1924 peep into the engineroom to see and hear those whizzing engines at work was a worthwhile experience. Three Babock & Wilcox boilers, two hopper-fed and one hand-fed standby, produced 150 psi steam. Two condensers converted exhaust steam back into hot water. Boiler water was pumped, either from the adjacent Witham or a deep well below the workshop floor. There was one engineer and one stoker on each shift. Generating began 5.30 am and finished 1 am when the batteries were switched in. Colliery coal slack, mixed with a little half-spent locomotive smokebox ash, bought cheaply from the GNR Locomotive Department, served as boiler fuel. A Grantham horse carter, under contract, took the slack coal down from the GNR Old Wharf goods yard. In Cleethorpes Electricity Station, the first steam engine was a Robey undertype portable. Two other Robeys worked in Bass-Gretton's Sleaford maltings, and one of them is preserved in the Bass Brewery Museum at Burton on Trent.

Steam was first considered for driving soil and rock excavators in the late 1870s. World pioneers in this field were Ruston & Proctor of Lincoln. In 1887 they sold seventy-one steam shovels, each capable of cutting a half cubic yard at each grab, for making the Manchester Ship Canal. It was the usual practice for digger engines to have two cylinders, one on either side of the winding drum shaft, with slide valves and Stephenson valve gear. Steam excavators and shovels were used in opencast iron ore mines around Frodingham and in the south-west near Grantham. Extraction was at its highest level during the Second World War, but after 1947 the higher grade imported ores from Sweden, Canada, Australia, South America and North Africa were increasingly used. Quarrying ceased by 1974 in the Grantham area, and at Normanby Park in the early 1980s.

There were big concentrations of industrial locomotives at the steels works and iron ore workings around Scunthorpe, and up to ten working at Colsterworth, Denton and Harlaxton, south-west of Grantham. Of these, *Ajax*, *Harlaxton*, *Rhondda*, *Gunby* and *Holwell* no 3 are now preserved in museums. In the mid-1920s a narrow gauge Hudswell Clark & Co, Leeds, 0-6-0 outside cylinder locomotive, no 11 on the stock list of Stanton Ironworks, Derbyshire, was in the Denton Park ironstone workings. Alongside the between-frames Stephenson valve gear was a boiler feed pump actuated by an eccentric on the driving axle, with the usual injector fitted on the firebox top. Two Ross pop-type safety valves released pressure in excess of 150 psi. In common with most industrial locomotives this one had no cold air deflecting brickarch in the firebox. Caythorpe had one locomotive, *Munition*, an 0-4-0 side tank made by Hawthorne Leslie 1918, sold when the quarry closed in 1946. Other locations where these small locomotives worked were for the Air Ministry at Cranwell; at the Bass, Ratcliff & Gretton's maltings at Sleaford; the sugar beet factories at Bardney, Brigg and Spalding; the Humber Brick & Tile Works at Barton on Humber; and for the Central Electricity Board at Keadby generating station.

# Steam and water

In 1802, an early date in the steamboat era, Wm Howden & Son built in their Grand Sluice Works at Boston, a small steam engine for turning the paddles on a Witham vessel. The first Gainsborough-Hull steamship service was inaugurated by the Glasgow-built *Caledonia* in 1814. Whereas sailing packets took three or four days, and sometimes a week on that run, with steam it was done in a day. Soon Gainsborough had its own 'steam-side' workshops and in 1815 the tug *Maria* was fitted there with a beam engine, making it possible to bring ships up the river against an ebb tide. Those early boats usually had twin engines, having short, large-diameter cylinders, with a boiler located below each one. At Lincoln by 1822 the paddle boat *Earl of Warwick* plied daily on the Witham with freight and passengers to and from Boston. This service ceased with the coming of the Great Northern Railway in 1848. Below the Grand Sluice at Boston, the steam packets *Lizzie* and *Annie* were running a goods-only service to Wisbech and London by 1890.

A Humber steam ferry was provided in the 1830s by the Barrow, New Holland and Goxhill ferries. This undertaking became the Humber Ferries Company, which was bought in 1846 for £21,000 by the Manchester, Sheffield & Lincolnshire Railway (later the GCR) to run the New Holland-Hull ferry from 1848. In 1850, the new paddle steamer *Sheffield*, built by H. E. Smith of Gainsborough and fitted with oscillating cylinder engines supplied by J. & G. Rennie, was delivered to the Great Central Railway for the Humber ferries. This service only ceased with the building of the 1978 Humber Bridge.

The paddle steamer *Tattershall Castle*, withdrawn from the Humber service in 1973, is now preserved at King's Reach on the Thames Embankment. The engine was made by the Central Marine Engine Works, West Hartlepool, a three-cylinder, direct acting compound engine which ran at 45 rpm and developed 1200 indicated horsepower whilst using steam at 204 psi. The three-flue Scotch-type boiler burnt 40 tons of coal a day. There is also a small two cylinder vertical high speed steam engine, made by Clarke Chapman of Gateshead, for generating an electrical supply for the vessel.

Steam trawlers were first tried at Grimsby in 1856, giving power also to the deck winches for hauling in nets. Under steam the fishing fleet grew apace, and by 1955 Grimsby trawlers caught 2 million cwts of fish annually, making this premier fish market in the world. The first diesel-engined trawlers appeared in the late 1930s, but it took another forty years to displace steam entirely. The Boston Deep Sea Fishing & Ice Company was formed in 1885, when Earles of Hull built them eight steam trawlers. Eventually the fleet grew to 35, with repair and boiler shops for their maintenance. The engineroom complement of a steam trawler was chief and second engineers and two firemen on shift work. Rickmer Werft of Bremerhaven supplied some steam trawlers to Grimsby owners in 1956. The triple expansion, totally enclosed engines, with forced-feed lubrication to all main bearings, proved splendid power units. One interesting feature was an exhaust steam-driven turbine that fed fourth-stage residual power into the propeller shaft. It was reckoned by British United Trawlers that those German engines burnt only 9½ tons of fuel oil daily, compared with 12 tons in British engines. Sufficient boiler feed water was carried for a three week trip, although a limited topping-up with sea water was allowed.

The first of the county's drainage steam pumps was erected at Sutton St Edmunds in 1820. Another engine was at the same time under construction in Murray & Fenton's Leeds works for installation in Borough Fen, to lift water into an eastwards flowing drain; where the cut enters Lincolnshire a mile south of Crowland, the hamlet is called The Engine. That early beam engine had a short life, because in 1832 the New Cut for the month of the River Nene provided natural drainage for that area.

During the period 1824-1850 many new steam pumphouses were built in the Fens. Pode Hole, two miles west of Spalding, was in the lowest part of Deeping Fen, where the North and South Drove Drains met. There were two huge, 4 psi steam pressure beam engines; the *Holland*, built by the Butterley Iron Co of Derbyshire, had a 44 inch diameter cylinder with an eight foot stroke, and rated 80 horsepower; the 60 horsepower *Kesteven*, by Fenton & Murray, had a 24 foot, 22 rpm flywheel. Each drove a scoop wheel which, in the case of the *Holland* engine, was 20 feet in diameter. Together the two wheels, lifting against a five foot head, poured 563 tons of water a minute into the Vernatts Drain which empties into the tidal Welland below Spalding. In the museum section of the present pumping station is an outline drawing of the 1885 steam *Hedgehog*, a portable-engined cable-hauled barge with spiked digging wheels, used for deepening the Welland and Glen rivers.

Steam was finally overtaken by internal combustion engine and electricity. But, while today its surviving engines are preserved by museums and collectors, this was the power behind the industrial and agricultural revolution which made Britain Great.

*FRONT COVER: Threshing day on Benjamin Bowser's Manor Farm at Scothern near Lincoln in February 1939. The engine was probably 8 nhp 1912 Ruston & Proctor no 44836, belonging to William Bowser of Greetwell Hall. The sounds associated with threshing would be the gentle, undulating puffing of the engine, the hum of the drum, and the click-clap of the straw jack's long, rectangular chains. Sidney Cash hand-forks unthreshed sheaves towards the drum's self-feeder. Behind him Edgar Gothorpe builds the straw stack, whilst Sidney Poulger peers through the straw jack. A housing estate now stands on this site. (LE)*

*One of a series of cartoons of 1835 by Alkens, ridiculing the over-optimistic hopes that steam power would usher in a life of ease. In the event, the men who worked steam ploughs had a hard life. (YRM)*

*The stand of Richard Hornsby of Grantham at the Great Exhibition of 1851 in Hyde Park, London. Interesting features of this well proportioned portable engine are the large flywheel suitable for a slow running engine, feed water heater in the chimney base, one-eccentric valve gear, enclosure of the cylinder within the firebox steam space, and adoption of a multi-tubular boiler instead of return tube type. (KM)*

*An 1857 engraving of Clayton & Shuttleworth's Stamp End Works at Lincoln, with canalised River Witham in foreground. From around 1820, it had been the wharf for Clayton's Witham steam packet service to Boston. The firm was world famous for its threshing machinery: in 1895 they made an engine a day, and by 1906 claimed a total output of 98,000 threshing machines. (HB)*

*Three-wheeled Wm Tuxford traction engine, fitted experimentally with the flap-footed Boydell Endless Railway Company's wheels, on trial in 1857 in Tuxford's works field, Boston. The wheels, aimed at spreading weight over a larger surface, were noisy and soon banged themselves to pieces. A chimney top spark arrestor suggests either a straw or wood burning engine intended for the Cuban or West Indian markets. The steersman, unable to see his front wheel, needed the direction pointer to guide him. The twin vertical cylinders are below the steeple-like slide bar covers behind the steersman. The boiler had one large oval flue tube between firebox and a dry-back chamber (metal plate without any water behind it) from which six round tubes led fire gases back to the smoke box end under the chimney. At that time Tuxfords, with 600 workers, were the largest employers of labour in Boston. (SM)*

*An 1857 engraving of Wm Tuxford's Boston & Skirbeck Ironworks alongside the Maud Foster Drain. The eight-sailed windmill is a reminder that the firm combinjed flour milling and baking with their agricultural engineering business. Tuxfords were given to much experimental engineering; they made good portables, land drainage and factory steam engines, but never came up with a market-winning traction engine. (HB)*

*Threshing on Captain Hoff's estate at Scremby near Spilsby in the 1890s. The wooden spoked wheels of the portable marks it as an early Marshall. The young driver wears a stiff celluloid collar easily washed with a soapy cloth and fashionable with workmen of the period. Eleven men and a water-carrying boy represented a normal threshing gang. The stack would take a day and a half to thresh. During the spring and early summer break from threshing, the engine drove the estate woodyard's circular saw. (HW)*

*Threshing day at Gipple Cottages, Syston near Grantham about 1900, with an 1870s Clayton & Shuttleworth portable. Georgie Watson (1852-1938), commonly known about Barkston as Engine Driver Watson was, with his Mill Farm uncle, joint owner of the tackle. The bowler-hatted man is Mr Clark, Farm Bailiff to Sir John Henry Thorold, for whom the threshing was being done. As Gipple well was a hundred feet deep, it is likely that the water cart was filled at the Grange Farm with its water-pumping windmill. (HB)*

*Clayton & Shuttleworth no 42787 general purpose engine of 1910, rated 7 nhp, looks after herself whilst gently puffing away when threshing at Sutterton in 1935. Grease tin, drum riddles, spark arrestor, oiling-up ladder and other paraphernalia litter the foreground. Some threshing engines were shy steamers in a strong side wind, and the large dark sheet at rear could be a wind shield. First owned by W. Westmoreland of Kirton, this engine passed to Samual Dawson around 1920, and he was the contractor owner at this threshing. It was last licensed 1948 by Thompson & Brown, Stoke Ferry, Norfolk. (BDS)*

This Hornsby of Grantham 6 nhp engine no 6317 of 1887 was sold new to a North Walsham purchaser. Here in 1935 it belonged to contractor Daniel Stanton, ready to thresh two bean stacks at Thurlby near Bourne. By 1900 Hornsbys had given up making traction engines in favour of oil-engined tractors for threshing work. Features of the engine are narrow spoked front wheels set well back, Watt-style two-ball heavy governor, and regulator valve on cylinder block with external, heat-losing pipe leading to left side valve chest. What thousands of tons of grain of all kinds this engine threshed over fifty-seven years in village stackyards before being broken up in 1944 by Peterborough scrapman G. Evans! Bob Gibbons, a Cambridgeshire contractor, often remarked how Hornsby no 6537, an 8 nhp of 1889, exhibited the remarkable feature that the harder she was worked, the less coal she burnt — and it was never found out why this happened. (BDS)

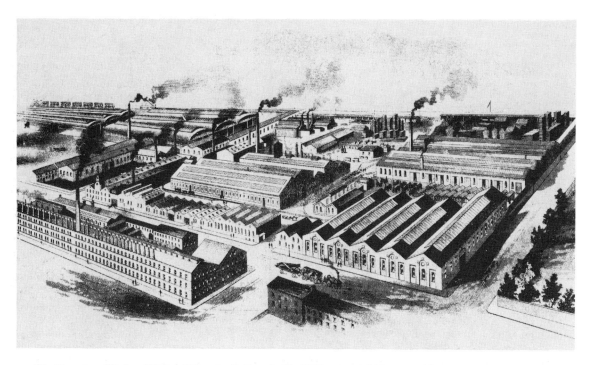

*The Grantham Works of Richard Hornsby & Son, Ltd in 1891, when 1,500 men and boys were employed, making 'The Firm' the town's best source of employment. The works were to the east of the Great Northern Railway, and on both sides of the old Great North Road. The 1860 blacksmith's shop (bottom left) had fifty-two smith's hearths, each having a short chimney above the third storey windows. A sheet metal weather-vane, shaped as a portable steam engine, swung from the south-west corner of the building until the devastating fire of 1960. (DNR)*

*Foster 7 nhp no 2827 of 1903, a really smart and businesslike engine, belted to the threshing drum beside a long-strawed wheat stack at Baston near Bourne in 1935. Daniel Stanton kept his tackles in a yard adjacent to the White Horse pub at Baston. He bought this engine new and it remained with him until scrapped in 1957 by Mr Roe, a Whittlesea scrapman. Foster's engines were not only powerful, but they also had a good reputation as nice steady engines before a threshing drum. A spare five-bladed chaff cutter wheel stands in the right foreground, and behind is the corn sack weighing machine. (BDS)*

*Massive class ZHS 20 nhp Fowler compound 1917 plough engine no 13863 Arran Chief, owned in 1920 by Frank Cooke, farmer and steam cultivation contractor of Town End Manor, Spalding. Sister engine no 13862 King Edward also had a potato name. Mr Cooke, a lover of steam power, in partnership with his son F. H. Cooke, of Gosberton, operated four sets of Fowler tackle. Immediately after the harvest these sets, manned by sixteen men, ploughed 1,000 acres of corn stubble in ten days in September 1920. Arran Chief had 8½ ins and 14 ins x 12 ins cylinders, Firth's special valve gear, an AA6 type boiler, smokebox superheater coils, and 600 yards of wire rope. Tom Redden, the foreman, is on the left. In 1938 the pair of engines were sold for £280 to Bomford & Evershed, dredging contractors of Salford Priors in Warwickshire (TR)*

*During July 1857, James Robson's farm at Brackenborough near Louth was the scene of extended trials with an 1856 Burrell-built engine. Described as a 'Steam Horse', it was fitted with experimental anti-bogging wheels designed by Mr Boydell of the Endless Railway Co, London. The trials took place over 23 acres of clayland clover stubble, baked hard by a drought and difficult to work. Overseas visitors from Cuba, Russia, Germany and Sweden looked on, and hundreds of county people also came every day. This early engine demonstrated with ploughs, a cultivator, clod crusher, harrows, sub-soiler, draining and trenching ploughs, and impressed by hauling four wagons loaded with chalk and soil up a steep incline. The way in which the flat-footed engine entered a yard, passed along a narrow lane, and turned neatly into an awkward gateway was also much admired. The rate of ploughing was just under an acre per hour. (DNR)*

*Fowler 1925 class AA7 twenty-tons compound 18 nhp plough engine no 16053 John owned by A. H. Carter of Tydd St Giles, seen here ploughing corn stubble in the Fens in 1935. Derek Stoyel of the Road Locomotive Society made a cycle tour of the Fens in 1935, photographing all the engines he could find. After exhibiton at the Peterborough Show in 1925, this tackle was driven to Tydd St Giles where Mr Carter threw a celebration party for all the village. In 1946 the pair of engines 16053/4, John and Michael, were bought by Herbert Thorlby of Eveden, and sold to the Museum of Lincolnshire Life in 1979. (BDS)*

*Aveling & Porter plough engines were thin on the ground in Lincolnshire. This is their 8 nhp, 15 tons 1909 compound no 6818, owned by B. N. and C. E. Smith of Spalding, ready for work at Guthram Gowt between Pinchbeck West and Bourne in 1935 when steam cultivation was in decline. For a period Aveling & Porter followed the unusual practice of a flat 8 nhp rating to their compound plough engines. The pair of engines nos 6817/8 were new to G. R. LeGrys, Heveningham, Suffolk, and went to the Smiths in 1919. They were sold again in 1944 to steam plough devotee J. K. Gandy of Thurlby, who last licensed them 1947. Note the even wind of the wire rope. (BDS)*

*Steam cultivating tackle, owned by well-known steam plough preservationist, the late H. R. Roads of Caxton, Cambs, standing in Ward & Dale's former engine winter parking ground in June 1960. He began rounding up unwanted sets before 1939, eventually saving ten tackles, many of them based in Lincolnshire. The maltings of Bass-Gretton, the Burton on Trent brewers, are in the background. During the 1960s the whole of this redundant tackle was moved to the family farm at Orwell, Cambs by Mr Road's son, Charles, and subsequently sold to steam plough fans for preservation. (HB)*

*John Fowler 1876 single cylinder 14 nhp plough engine no 2909 exploded violently at 8.30 am on 1 August 1913 at Belmont Farm, Benniworth in the Wolds. The London-made 100 psi wrought-iron boiler was well-worn down with 37 years' hard work, last properly examined in 1911 and uninsured. The explosion ripped open a twenty-six inches old fracture running along a rivet line, and upwards of eight inches into an area of eroded barrell plate. Foreman T. Blanchard, driver Harry Marshall and cultivator steersman Herbert Lowiss were only thirty to forty yards away from the engine busy splicing a broken cable; they were severely scalded and Marshall suffered a broken leg. For three days they were nursed by Mrs Tharratt, the farmer's wife, at Belmont House, before a horse-drawn ambulance took them the sixteen miles to Lincoln Hospital, where Blanchard died five days later. The boiler pressure had been lifted to 120 psi and the safety valve was blowing off madly when the boiler burst. The Board of Trade Inspector found T. E. Frearson and F. O. Bartholomew, of West Barkwith, joint owners of the tackle, responsible for negligence in boiler maintenance. (DNR)*

*The dome-shaped casting over this roller's front roll forks marks it as a Marshall machine, and the Gainsborough firm were probably the county's most prolific roller makers. The roller is outside the old Public Hall, High Street, Scunthorpe in 1899. The three bearded men follow the railway-making navvies' custom of tying their trousers below the knee, in order to lift the bottoms off the ground. (HLS)*

*In 1947 Aveling-Barford of Grantham made the final but unsuccessful attempt to modernise steam rollers to challenge diesel power. Although this unique roller performed well when tested in the works yard, the purchase price was too high for a customer, either Indian or East Asian, who contemplated a large order for both steam and diesel rollers, each having as many interchangeable parts as possible. The order was then given for diesel rollers only. Principal features were: rear-mounted four cylinder V type 1200 rpm steam engine, coupled directly to a diesel roller gearbox, cylinders 4 ins x 3½ ins stroke, boiler pressure 200 psi., 132 tubes 1ft 6¾ ins long and 1½ ins diameter, plus sixteen 1¾ ins stay tubes, 5.24 sq ft firegrate area and a total heating surface of 97 sq ft. (A-B)*

*Clayton overtype steam wagons, on wooden wheels shod with solid rubber, at Catteneres on the Cambrai Section of the Western Front 1917 during WW1. These army wagons took munitions, by night, from the railheads to the front fighting line. The side sheet tarpaulins served for weather protection and also as blackout screens. (RSM)*

*This 1920 cross-boilered steam wagon no 1220 was made by the Yorkshire Engine Co of Leeds. It is seen here in the 1930s, in the ownership of Jack Rundle of New Bolingbroke, hauling a river or estuary dredging barge on behalf of Mornement & Ray, dredging contractors of Boston. The special low-hung transporter vehicle, with front and rear bogies as designed by Jack, was made in Foster's works. Because of the limited road clearance, when likely obstructions were met, planks were placed under the bogie wheels to lift the load. The heavy ballast on the wagon gave sufficient road adhesion for braking down steep hills. (JR)*

*This is overtype steam wagon no 32746 built by Richard Garrett, Leiston, Suffolk in 1915. It was two speed, chain driven, and powered by a compound piston valve, 400 rpm, 200 psi steam pressure engine. Water capacity was 120 gallons and the bunker held 3 cwt of coal. Inside the ugly box atop the smokebox was the superheater. In 1935 it lay derelict in the paddock of transport contractor and brickmaker J. D. Kent on Mareham Lane, Sleaford. (BDS)*

*J. A. Cole of Roxholme Hall near Sleaford bought two new late 1890s 7 nhp Ruston-Proctor traction engines to start a threshing business. Two of his sons turned the undertaking into Cole Bros, building up the firm as general engineers, engine dealers, threshing, cultivating, road rolling and steam haulage contractors. In 1925 the partnership was broken up, with Arthur M. Cole the sole proprietor. He died, aged 94½, in June 1984, but the business still continues. This c1924 photograph shows four of Cole Bros wagons in their Sleaford Yard, left-right: Allchin (Northampton) AH 0541 made around 1917/18 and scrapped 1928 by Joseph Stockdale of East Markham, Notts; Foden no 1695 of 1908; Clayton no 48450 of 1920; and Foster no 14467 of 1920. (DNR)*

*Lincoln showman Fred Warren leans against the front wheel of Smiths & Warrens' Burrell no 1985, Mona, an 8 nhp single crank compound (it was unusual to find a single crank compound in showmen's use) new to them in 1897. The outfit was on the point of leaving the 1908 Coningsby Feast. The old fashioned three-abreast roundabout, with centre engine, is on the second truck. This six-truck road train of converted horse-drawn vehicles is very long; later the legal limit was three trucks and a water cart. Jack Rundle, son of the village parson, stands at the right. (HR)*

*Lord Ancaster, descendant of the steam pioneer Lord Willoughby d'Eresby, owned Aveling & Porter compound road locomotive Long Tom no 5660 of 1904, seen here sawing wood at Grimsthorpe Castle c1905. The A. & P. three tons, 3 nhp, convertible no 5541 of the same year, had proved under-powered, so larger Long Tom came in part exchange from E. Foley of Bourne. Later the engine went to C. Miles & Son, threshing contractors of Stamford. (DNR)*

*A Hornsby 1890s single cylinder traction engine serving as a heavy load test piece during adhesion trials with one of the firm's early 40 ihp diesel-engined and tracked tractors of c1909 in the works yard at Grantham. This was a forerunner of military tracked vehicles. David Roberts, Hornsby's clever inventor, concerned with the development of tracked vehicles, received no official recognition for his part in producing the 1915 British Army tanks. (LLS)*

*Richard Hornsby & Sons obtained an order in 1908 for a tracked steam engine for hauling coal over the frozen roads of the Yukon. As the Grantham firm no longer made steam engines, Fosters of Lincoln made the steam side for Hornsbys to mount on their tracks. These are the 1910 trials on the Roman Ermine Street east of Grantham. This engine's boilerless remains were found in the 1970s by a Lincoln businessman on a fishing holiday, rusting in coastal pine woods in the north-west of Vancouver Islands. (HB)*

*Foster 1911 agricultural tractor (of the so called 'Plough Engine Project') powered by a Hornsby two-cylinder paraffin engine, in all likelihood on the Hornsby-Ackroyd solid fuel injection principle, now unfortunately credited to Dr Diesel. This heavy engine, fashioned too closely on cumbersome traction engines, was an experimental tractor intended for sale to an Argentine customer. The water tank over the exceptionally tall rear wheel and frontal radiator were part of the water cooling system. The final drive was through annular toothed rings, inside the inner edges of both hind wheels. It was this type of tractor, but with a Daimler engine, that sparked off the military tank idea in 1915.*
*(LLS)*

*This Marshall, Sons & Co road locomotive, made c1922, was a special job for the direct haulage of agricultural implements. This is probably in Egypt. Particular features are the tandem compound cylinders with the high pressure one in front, a steam dome, short connecting rods, a small diameter flywheel, brackets holding the cylinder block clear of the boiler barrel, and a force-feed pump on the belly tank, to take hot water from the adjacent feed-water heater and force it into the boiler. (MS)*

*This unusual Edwardian postcard, unfortunately undated, shows a large boiler manufactured by Marshall, Sons &*
*Co of Gainsborough, being moved by elephant power on its way to a tea factory in Ceylon. (DNR)*

*A 1925 Fowler B6 class 8 nhp road locomotive hauling a river gravel dredging barge through Barkston an 8 October 1933, on its way from Lincoln to London. Gwynnes Pumps Ltd, a Foster subsidiary, had built the barge in Foster's old engine works. The special load, too awkward for rail transit, had been contracted out by the LNER to Norman Box Ltd, Manchester steam hauliers. Note the electric lights, and also the stable lantern, hung below the belly tank, to cast a guiding beam on the roadside verge for the steersman's benefit at night. (HB)*

*Fowler 1906 class A4 compound road locomotive no 10589 hauls a boiler from Louth station to Smith's Soap Works in 1919. It was owned by Evan W. Macdonald who, around 1902, founded his Louth business of a country engineer and steam operator. He preferred the A4 type and at one time had two others, nos 9139 and 9887. He was a clever steam man, but was sometimes a difficult character to work with. His son, Dick, developed a flair for machinist's work and, on his father's death in 1963, became head of the firm, which still flourishes under grandson Glyn. Macdonalds also undertook threshing and steam cultivation, the latter with Fowler BBs Nos 14189/90. Evan is second from the right; his son, Evan, stands in front of the hind wheel and a grandson sits on the wheel. (DNR)*

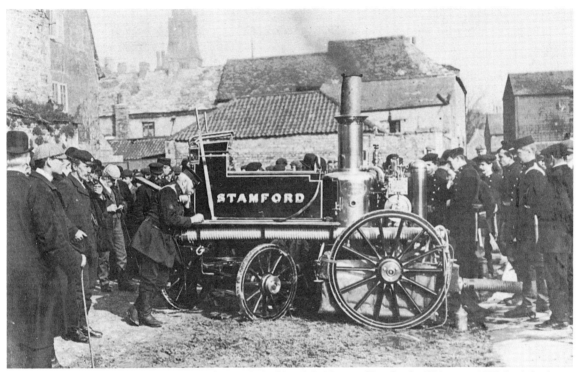

*A Stamford horse-drawn steam fire-engine, made by Shand & Mason of London in 1890, at an 1895 fire brigade demonstration beside the Mill Stream on Bath Row. Two vertical simple-acting cylinders to the rear of the upright boiler had below them a pair of centrifugal pumps, adjustable either for suction or pressure action. This enabled the engine to pick up water from a stream or pond and at the same time to deliver a high pressure discharge into the seat of a fire. Also in 1895, C. F. Young of Abbey Farm, Swineshead, used a J. C. Merryweather, London, fire engine to spray eighty tons of fen dyke water an hour for experimental irrigation. (LLS)*

On 29 June 1903, at 12.30 pm, fire broke out in the pavilion bar of the Great Central Railway's tar-boarded Cleethorpes Pier, and the 880 seat concert hall was gutted. Two steam fire engines attended; the Shand Mason type belonging to Grimsby Town Council, and the unidentified one from the railway company's Grimsby Docks. The tide was out and it was difficult to haul the engines over the muddy foreshore to the end of the Pier; the water cart bogged down halfway and there was only a trickle of water from the pier main. In desperation the town brigade dropped the suction pipe in a gulley of sea water, picking up much sand with the water with dire effects on the engine. Members of the fire committee had a lively meeting after the fire. One said the equipment was more suitable for watering a garden, and another was alarmed at the rumoured expense of sending the engine back to the London makers for repairs. Feelings cooled with the announcement that only one of the boiler's 130 tubes had burst and the town engineer had done the work himself. (DNR)

*Every dinner hour and 5.30 pm finishing time, the outpouring of Marshall's engineering employees from the Britannia Works was a familiar sight in Gainsborough. The terrace houses where they lived were only a few minutes' walk away. Those who remained in the factory at dinner times ate packed meals in winter, seeking warmth round blacksmith's furnaces. (DNR)*

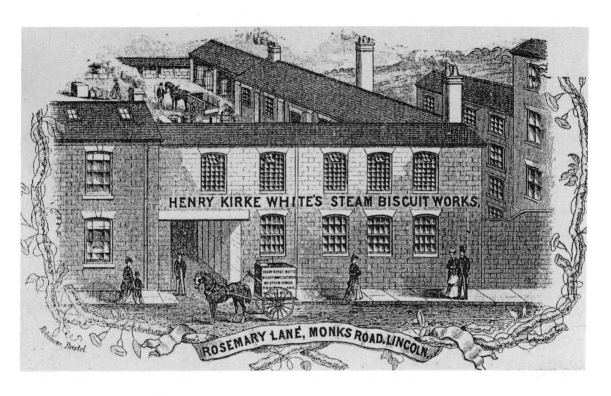

*In the 1890s Henry Kirke White of Lincoln proudly announced how up-to-date he was, by using steam power for the manufacture of biscuits. The legend on the horse-drawn cart is 'Biscuit Manufacturer by Steam Power'. He had retail shops in the High Street and Bailgate. (DNR)*

*The construction of Immingham Dock between 1906 and 1912 involved keeping over 100 boilers in steam daily for five years, for locomotives, steam excavators, cranes, pumps and portable engines. One notable machine was this steam-driven continuous bucket excavator. (EH)*

*Immingham Dock Electricity Generating Station in 1955, with four steam-driven turbo alternators. Three are BTH, Rugby, machines and that in the background is a 1924 English Electric, obtained in 1926 after service at the British Empire Exhibition at Wembley 1924-25. Each steam turbine is at the right of its electrical alternator. Steam passed through a succession of high speed turbine vanes, before exhausting onto a condenser. Advantages of turbines were avoidance of power losses in stopping and restarting pistons at the end of each stroke as in conventional steam engines, smooth quiet running, and high power-extraction efficiency. Increasing demands for electrical power at Immingham (which also supplied Grimsby Dock) were met by improvements, but the chimney was not large enough to serve additional boilers. When it was shown that Yorkshire Electricity Board bulk supplies would be cheaper, the station closed on 26 November 1957. (ABD)*

*The boilerhouse at Immingham Dock Power Station in 1955, showing the five 250 psi Babcock & Wilcox, Glasgow, water tube boilers. In 1932 these had replaced nine obsolete hand-fired Lancashire boilers installed during the construction of the dock. Slack coal fuel was fed from overhead hoppers down the large diameter sloping tubes into mechanical stokers. Moving firegrates (left foreground) carried the burning fuel under water-filled boiler tubes and tipped dead clinker into ash hoppers. The swan-headed air intake pipes and the horizontal ducting over the heads of the two officials were part of an unsuccessful trial to increase firegrate draughting. Steam was provided for electrical generation and for four steam-driven hydraulic pumps, one of which remained in use until 1956. (ABP)*

55

*Busy Trent river traffic, both sail and steam, is evident from this 1840s engraving of Furley's Wharf and works at Gainsborough. Beam-type engines made in Boulton & Watt's Soho, Birmingham factory, were installed in the earliest river boats, but later, locally built ones were used. Boiler pressures were a mere 10-20 psi. (HTDM)*

*This quiet river scene is on the Trent below Gainsborough, with a small propeller-fitted steam tug hauling the three-masted sea-going schooner G. R. Berg along the ebb tide. Marine steam engines exhausted quietly into condensers, avoiding any chimney 'chuffs'. (EWC)*

*The steam tug Ferryman tows a string of four heavily laden keels up the Trent in the early 1920s. This medium-sized tug would be powered by a small compound or triple expansion engine, with crankshaft in line with the propeller shaft. Engine-rooms, cramped for space, were occupied by one engineer, who stoked his own boiler furnace. (EWC)*

*The paddle steamer Gainsborough splashes along the Trent about 1912 with a party of excursionists, a popular way of sightseeing. These boats were powered either by an oscillating or a plain reciprocating engine, conveniently windowed for passengers to admire the highly polished and thumping machinery. (HLS)*

*The heavy snows of late winter 1947 were followed by a rapid thaw in April, and the Trent broke its banks at a number of places below Gainsborough. Steam-driven cranes on barges were brought in from Holland to unload stone from barges for bank repair work. The coal supply barge also lies alongside. (DNR)*

*In the aftermath of the disastrous storm surge of 31 January 1953, there was urgent need to repair and renew the many miles of broken sea defences along the Lincolnshire coast, before the next spring tides. All forms of power were pressed into use, including steam for piledriving the new defences. Wreaths of smoke and steam rose along the coast, either side of the Mablethorpe Convalescent Home, throughout most of February. (DNR)*

*This unusual machine, with central steam engine and 60 foot circular conveyor belt, was designed by A. P. Grossmith and made by Rubery, Owen & Co, Victoria Ironworks, Darlaston. It was in use in an ironstone quarry, possibly near Scunthorpe, about 1909. Fed by the steam digger (right), it conveyed overburden to the worked-out side of the pit. (BSC)*

*This Ruston horizontal-boilered steam shovel was loading iron ore into railway wagons for the British Steel Corporation in the Scunthorpe – Frodingham area in the 1920s. Before the days of steam shovels, quarrymen used hand picks, sledgehammers, iron crowbars and gunpowder to win iron ore. (BSC)*

*A rail-mounted Ruston steam shovel at work in a Scunthorpe ironstone quarry about 1930. One of the two cylinders with its connecting rod and disc crank can be seen, and the fireman holds a shovelful of coal ready to charge the fire through the sideways-placed firehole. Note the rickety foundation of short rails. (BSC)*

*This 1930s steam-powered Ruston-Bucyrus dragline was one of the last machines of its kind. It is transferring overburden from an iron ore face near Scunthorpe in what appears to be a demonstration for visitors. Although retaining a horizontal boiler, it is mounted on caterpillar tracks. The excavator-making side of Rustons had affiliated with the American excavator firm Bucyrus-Erie in 1930. Ruston-Bucyrus closed in 1985 (BSC)*

*Early steam navvy, maker unknown, excavating a water reservoir for the WW1 military camp in Belton Park, Grantham, about 1915. The unusually low positioning hides any wheeled undercarriage it may have had. (LLS)*

*At the outbreak of WWI, Earl Brownlow placed Belton Park at the disposal of the War Office, and a standard gauge, freight only, light railway was laid down to serve the large wooden-hutted military camp built there. This photograph of 1916 shows a tiny, low-powered saddle-tank locomotive hauling wagons around the camp. From a connection with the GNR main line south of Gonerby Lane overbridge, the track ran across grass fields, and un-gated level crossings on Gonerby Lane and the A607, to enter the park half a mile north of Manthorpe. All trains then reversed direction, and ran downhill over a new timber bridge spanning the River Witham. There was a fatal accident on the line in August 1915 when Private Harry Stromberg of the Manchester Regt got his foot fast in a track fitting at the Londonthorpe Lane level crossing. He was knocked down by the leading of four loaded granite wagons pushed by an engine at the rear, as there were no facilities for turning the engine. This line was lifted 1919-20. (LLS)*

In 1899, Aveling & Porter mounted the superstructure of their compound traction engine no 4399 on standard-gauge rail wheels for use as an 0-4-0 yard-shunting locomotive. Following the amalgamation of Aveling-Barford in 1931, the odd little locomotive was taken to Grantham. This c1938 photograph shows a Ropsley villager called Johnson driving it in the works yard. Power was transmitted from the crankshaft through a large encased cogwheel to annular toothed rings, bolted on the insides of both right hand side road wheels. The non-rotative rod between axle centres held the cog drive in the correct mesh. Rickety railings around the bunker prevented the driver from falling off backwards should he buffer up sharply against wagons. As there was little space on the driver's platform for coal, small heaps were placed about the yard. When Johnson retired in 1946 the engine was stored until 1949 and then sold as scrap to the Grantham Boiler & Crank Co. (A-B)

*This standard-gauge industrial two-cylinder 0-4-0 locomotive of 1946, supplied new by Peckett & Sons of Bristol to Aveling-Barford replaced A. & P. no 4399. The work of this shunter was in the works yard and making trips to and from the LNER up-freight yard, using a connection passing under the Great North Road. Albert Willis, former LNER engine cleaner, fireman and driver, is on the footplate. His duties included such running repairs as fitting a new blast pipe or retubing the boiler. On Monday mornings he came on duty at 4 am in order to light up and raise steam in time for the opening of the works at 8 am. This Peckett, in first class order, was sold as scrap to metal merchant Charles Spick in 1963. (AW)*

*Robert Stephenson & Co of Newcastle made this 1937 two cylinder 0-6-0 standard-gauge saddle-tank locomotive no 4156, here shunting molten iron at Frodingham Mill sidings in 1957 for the Appleby-Frodingham Steel Co. In addition to internal work within the yards and quarries of the ten ore-mining and iron-making concerns around Scunthorpe and Frodingham, these engines ran trips to and from main-line exchange sidings. There were about 150 industrial locomotives in 1950, running over the 250 miles of private track, and each company had its own locomotive repair shop. (JJF)*

*This 0-6-0 inside-cylindered standard-gauge saddle-tank locomotive Bletcher, built in 1870 by Manning Wardle of Leeds, works no 318, was no 3 on the 5¼ miles Air Ministry Works and Buildings light railway (1915-1956) between Cranwell aerodrome and Sleaford. It was first used in 1919. This photograph of 1921 shows (L to R): on engine — cleaner C. Hill, driver J. Lister; on ground — guard J. Frier, foreman engineer T. Jackson and fireman C. Ellis. The carriages came secondhand from the GNR London suburban area. Third class return fare was 3d. Two locomotives were needed during the hey-day years of 1919-1923 for the 13-coach passenger trains on Saturdays. 'Bus competition led to withdrawal of passenger services in 1927. (RAFCC)*

*Unloading the steam trawler Weelsby in Grimsby Fish Dock in the 1920s. Engine-room staff, shut up with steam engines and boilers inside the confined hulls of trawlers, had a wet, noisy and unpleasant job. If a boiler tube leaked at sea, the trawler hove to, fires were dropped, and a stoker crawled through the still hot furnace-flue to fix a far end blanking-off disc (known as a 'stopper') over the leaking tube. The two-ended stopper was then tightened up from the near, or stoke-hole, end of the boiler. (HLS)*

*Grimsby steam trawler GY 209 Empyrean coaling at the coaling plant in no 3 Fish Dock in the late 1930s. By 1939 a million tons of best Nottinghamshire and Yorkshire steam coal a year were burnt by trawlers, although oil-fired boilers were coming in. Fish was stowed in the empty coal space on the return run. (DNR)*

*Grimsby steam trawler Wellard was a coal-fired vessel built before WW2, during which she was a convoy escort. Her wartime gear included a 4.7 ins gun, depth charges and sonar gear. In February 1942 she sailed alone to America where, along with twenty other converted trawlers, she guarded US coastal convoys between Key West in Florida and Halifax, Canada; six of these trawlers were sunk by German U-boats. In October 1942, sailing via Brazil, the Gold Coast and the Cape, Wellard continued her convoy service in the Indian and South Atlantic oceans. (HLS)*

*Grimsby steam trawler GY 3542 leaves the Fish Dock on another trip. Note the bridge in front of the funnel for better navigation. In the background is the Grimsby Dock Tower, modelled on the companile at Sienna, used to supply hydraulic power to the lock gates. (DNR)*

*These two large engines, made by Easton, Amos & Anderson of London, were installed at Lade Bank on the Hobhole Drain in 1867 as the first steam pumps in the East Fen. Named Will o' th' Wisp and Waterwitch, they were linked to fast running, high capacity centrifugal pumps. Bottom left is one 30 x 30 inch cylinder with parallel motion and slide-bar-less piston and connecting rod. The tall toothed mitre wheel fixed on the overhead crankshaft drives the smaller one on the vertical shaft of the submerged Appold pump. Each 120 hp engine ran at 38 rpm, using 50 psi steam, distributed by Stephenson valve gear. There were six Lancashire boilers, each 23 x 6½ feet. During the bad flood of 1875, both engines ran continuously for seven days and nights and burnt 300 tons of coal. At periods of peak demand, two drivers and a boy were needed to man the engineroom. Diesel engines were installed in 1939 and the steam machinery scrapped. (HB)*

This pair of 1852 Easton & Amos, London, grasshopper-type beam engines drove a scoop wheel until about 1930 in West Butterwick pumping station. Water was lifted from the low-lying Isle of Axholme into the tidal Trent. The large centrally placed mitre wheel meshed with a train of gear wheels, which drove the scoop wheel outside the right hand wall. Diesel engine-driven Gwynnes centrifugal pumps, working against a 17 foot head, replaced steam around 1930. Note the oil lantern for illumination at night. Noises heard inside such pumphouses were low hissings from steam leaks, whirring of meshing cog wheels and the soughing sound of each exhaust into the condenser. (HB)

*Timberland pumphouse stands on the west bank of the River Witham, south of Kirkstead. The first steam engine, installed in 1839, was a 30 hp low pressure beam type, turning a 26 ft x 6 ft scoop wheel. It was superseded in 1881 by a tall, 50 hp high-pressure Tuxford condensing beam engine, driving a centrifugal pump. The cylinder was a 3 ft x 6 ft stroke model having a 24 ft flywheel weighing 13 tons. This was replaced in 1924 by a Foster vertical steam engine; the boiler, used as a diesel oil storage tank, still remains in the lean-to building on the right. Two Ruston diesels replaced the Foster engine in the 1930s, and are preserved in the main building as museum pieces. On the left are the discharge pipes from the three automatic electric pumps which now lift water 12 feet from Walcot Delph Fen into the River Witham beyond. (HB)*

*Frank Young, a Ward & Dale implement steersman, stands beside the plough and cultivator of a single cylinder engine-set of cultivating tackle in 1898. He was then eighteen and this was somewhere in the Boston area. These tackles normally used a five-furrow plough, so the six furrow one here would be as much as the engines could pull. (DAR)*

*The boilershop at Wm Foster's Lincoln Works about 1908. Here the special-grade boiler-quality steel was rolled into round barrels, or shaped into the rectangular firebox plate, drilled with tube or rivet holes, and complete boilers were delivered to the adjoining erecting shop. A pneumatic rivetter stands on the wooden trestle in right foreground. The long chassis across the foreground was the beginning of a steam wagon. Boilershops, noted for the frightful clangour set up by rivetting, caused many boilersmiths to go hard of hearing, or even stone deaf. (LLS)*

*Jack Rudd drives Fowler BB class plough engine no 15441 Lion whilst dredging a farm pond at Bolingbroke in 1978. The pair of engines 15441/2, new in 1920 to the Keisby Estate near Bourne, were once in Jack's charge. They are now owned by F. Coupland of Carrington. The cast-iron chimney came from the Oxford Steam Plough Co of Cowley and would out-live several chimneys rolled out of mild steel plate. (HB)*

*John Fowler 1872 single cylinder, friction drive, 12 nhp plough engine, after 63 years of hard work awaits scrapping in Ward & Dale's yard at Sleaford 1935. It started work in Scotland in the Elginshire Steam Cultivation Co before acquisition by Ward & Dale, who paired it with no 1556 in their no 15 set of tackle. It was these single-cylinder, loud-exhausting engines which saw the Sleaford firm through their busiest days. Interesting fetures are the heavy casting under the smokebox, which incorporated the top half of the ball and socket bearing for the front axle, the 350 yards only rope drum, and the whistle on top of the firebox. The crew's living van stands behind. (BDS)*

*George Elston (1857-1931) trained as a mechanic in Hornsby's works at Grantham, and afterwards became a threshing contractor at The Street, Welby. Between 1890 and 1900 he built, in a tiny lathe-fitted wooden hut behind his house, six of these miniature portables, and a small traction engine. These three-feet-long engines had a single cylinder 2⅛ ins x 2½ ins, and a seven-tube boiler pressed at 60 psi. Travelling showmen bought the first five for driving small organs, or pumps behind the jets of water supporting erratically-moving celluloid balls at shooting galleries. This particular engine is preserved by George Storer of Sawtry in Cambridgeshire, whose parents were neighbours of the Elstons. (GS)*

*LEFT: Rev Harness Rundle, vicar of New Bolingbroke, visiting his son Jack's threshing about 1936. Father and son both had an abiding interest in steam. Jack trained as an engineer, had a period handling showmen's engines and finally set up a threshing and haulage business in the village. The engine here is Robey 1908 single cylinder no 28172, a general-purpose type 7 nhp model. It was sold, with drum and elevator, for £1,100 in 1947, when Jack, faced with growing competition from combine harvesters, coupled with his own dislike for using motor tractors, sold the threshing side. Rundle's engineering works still exist at New Bolingbroke. (JR) RIGHT: Franklin E. Cheffins with Burrell showman's engine no 4000 Ex Mayor as it generates electricity on Edlington fairground near Doncaster in September 1931. A step-ladder was the easiest way to get into or down from the cab. The young boy was the son of Harry Tuby, owner and operator of the engine. (HB)*

*Chad Orris wearing his wide-awake hat as he drives a Garrett engine threshing at Rippingale in 1924. Owned by Mr Challands, no 25890 was a 7 nhp model of 1906. Chad's right hand is on the horizontal regulator and his left is over the screw rod of the handbrake, a useful fitting not found on all threshing engines. The reversing lever at centre is pushed fully into fore gear. The ladder against the chimney was handy for replacing the spark arrestor with the over-night damper plate. (LS)*

*Hay and straw-baling work was undertaken by threshing engines, using a special baling machine. This 1921 photograph shows Sneath & Sons tackle returning to Thurlby, near Bourne, after baling 12,749 tons 18 cwt on a 1915-19 government-directed job in Wiltshire, followed by a final stint on surplus army fodder around Devizes for a private contractor in 1919-21. The Clayton & Shuttleworth single-cylinder engine no 37150 is followed by the presser, and large and small living vans. Straw-hatted Mr Sneath stands beside his motor cycle combination. Driver Frank Orris and steersman W. Brown are on the engine. Sneath had bought this Clayton in 1915 from Foley of Bourne, and it was sold in 1930 to the Marsh threshermen of Aunsby in 1930. (LS)*

*This page, from the catalogue for the Royal Show at Lincoln in 1907, gives a good idea of the range of steam engines, pumps and boilers produced by Robey & Co Ltd at their Globe Works in the city, and of the diversity of steam as a source of power, especially in Lincolnshire. (DNR)*

# Index to Illustrations